PLAY MISSION PRAISE 2

Instrumental arrangements

Christopher Norton

Marshall Pickering
An Imprint of HarperCollins*Publishers*

Marshall Pickering is an imprint of
HarperCollins*Religious*,
part of HarperCollins*Publishers*,
77-85 Fulham Palace Road,
Hammersmith, London W6 8JB

1 3 5 7 9 10 8 6 4 2

ISBN 0 551 02955 2

Music and text set by Barnes Music Engraving Limited,
East Sussex, England

Printed and bound in Great Britain by
Scotprint Limited, Musselburgh, Edinburgh

A catalogue record for this book is available from the British Library

CONTENTS

Be still, for the presence of the Lord

MPC 50

Words and music: David J Evans

1 Be still, for the pre-sence of the Lord, the Ho - ly One, is here;
2 Be still, for the glo - ry of the Lord is shi - ning all a - round;
3 Be still, for the pow - er of the Lord is mov - ing in this place:

come bow be - fore Him now with re - ver - ence and fear:
He burns with ho - ly fire, with splen - dour He is crowned:
He comes to__ cleanse and heal, to mi - ni - ster His grace —

in Him no sin is found — we stand on ho - ly ground.
how awe - some is the sight – our ra - diant King of light!
no work too hard for Him. In faith re - ceive from Him.

Be still, for the pre-sence of the Lord, the Ho - ly One, is here.
Be still, for the glo - ry of the Lord is shi - ning all a - round.
Be still, for the pow - er of the Lord is mov - ing in this place.

Be still, for the presence of the Lord

Be still, for the presence of the Lord

Eb Melody II

Bass

Father God, I wonder

MPC 128

Words and music: Ian Smale
Keyboard arrangement: David Peacock

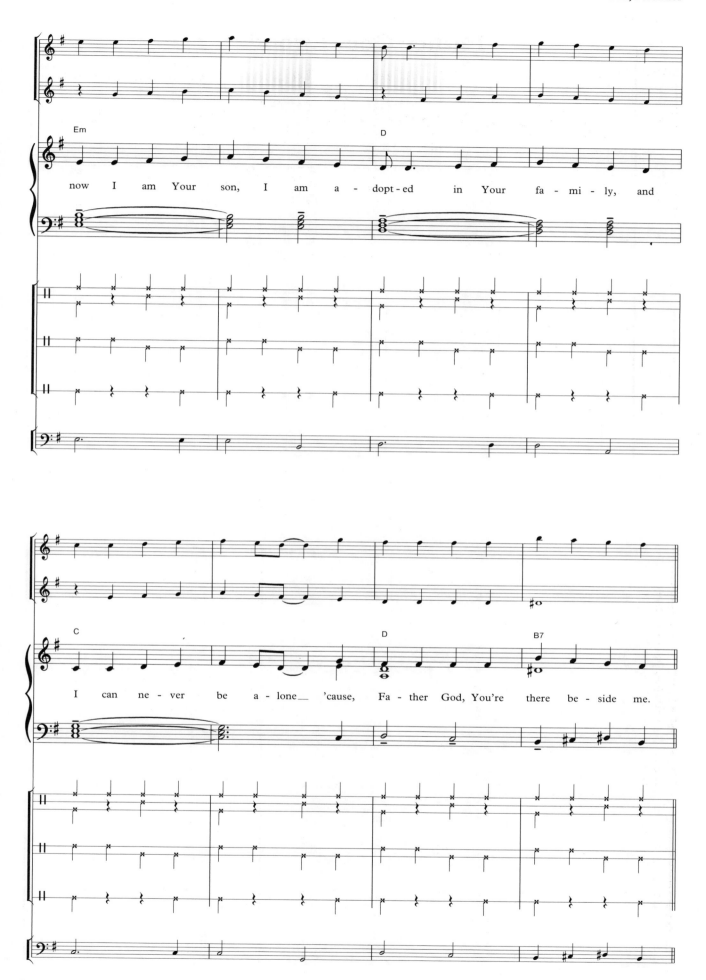

Father God, I wonder

I will sing Your prais - es, I will sing Your prais - es, I will

sing Your prais - es for ev - er - more. for ev - er - more.

Father God, I wonder

Father God, I wonder

He is exalted

MPC 217

Words and music: Twila Paris

He is exalted

He is exalted

He is exalted

Eb Melody II

Bass

I am a new creation

MPC 254

Words and music: Dave Bilbrough
Keyboard arrangement: David Peacock

I am a new cre-a-tion, no more in con-dem-na-tion,

here in the grace of God I stand.

I am a new creation

I am a new creation

I am a new creation

Majesty

MPC 454

Words and music: Jack Hayford

Majesty

Majesty

Majesty

Rejoice!

MPC 572

Words and music: Graham Kendrick

to Coda ⊕

A7sus   D   A/D   G/D   D   A/D   G/D   D

- my____ we a-rise! _____

A7   G/B   Bm   G/B   G/A

1 Now is the time for us___ to march up-on___ the land__   in - to our
2 God is at   work in us,___ His pur - pose to___ per-form __   build - ing a
3 Though we are weak, His grace is   ev - ery-thing we need __   we're made of

Rejoice!

Words and music: © 1983 Kingway's Thankyou Music, PO Box 75, Eastbourne, East Sussex BN23 6NW, UK. Used by permission

Rejoice!

MISSION PRAISE

Mission Praise was originally compiled for the Mission England campaign in 1984, and was especially designed to appeal to the broad range of churches taking part in the campaign. Its tremendous popularity led to two further collections, *Mission Praise 2* (1987) and the *Mission Praise Supplement*. In 1990 came *Mission Praise Combined*, drawing on the best of all three books to produce a definitive collection for church worship.

Features:

• a broad selection of traditional hymns and modern songs, combining the best of the old with the best of the new

• the most comprehensive collection available, with a total of 798 items

• items suitable for both choirs and music groups

• a wide range of hardwearing editions including hardback, paperback and spiral bindings

New!

Sing Mission Praise - a collection of attractive new vocal arrangements for 55 of the most popular worship songs from *Mission Praise Combined*

Play Mission Praise 1 - the first book in a new series of instrumental arrangements for *Mission Praise Combined*

Mission Praise Combined is available in the following editions:

Words edition	ISBN 0 551 01979 4	(single copy)
	ISBN 0 551 01977 8	(25 copy pack)
Easy-to-read words edition	ISBN 0 551 02627 8	
Large Print words edition	ISBN 0 551 01978 6	
Music edition	ISBN 0 551 01986 7	(hardback)
Musicians' edition vol. 1	ISBN 0 551 02266 3	(spiral bound)
Musicians' edition vol. 2	ISBN 0 551 02267 1	(spiral bound)
Musicians' edition vol. 3	ISBN 0 551 02268 X	(spiral bound)
Sing Mission Praise	ISBN 0 551 04010 6	
Play Mission Praise 1	ISBN 0 551 02954 4	